ABCmouse.com
Early Learning Academy

D1396623

Phonics:
Consonants and Vowels

ABCmouse.com *Early Learning Academy* **is the award-winning digital learning program that covers math, reading, science, social studies, art, music, and more for kids ages 2 to 8.**

With more than 10,000 individual Learning Activities and over 850 lessons across 10 levels, ABCmouse is a proven educational resource that is trusted by parents and teachers across the U.S. and around the world.

Go to
www.ABCmouse.com
to learn more.

ABC Mouse

TM & © 2020 Age of Learning, Inc.

ABCmouse.com

At-Home
LEARNING TIPS ☑

Dear Families,

The keys to successfully managing a "learn-at-home" situation are often related to time and space. Here are a few tips to ensure that you and your child are getting the most of your opportunities to learn at home.

Managing Time

☐ Establish a routine for your day. For example, plan to start "learning time" at the same time every day, and schedule consistent breaks for meals, exercise, and free time. Make that routine as similar to your child's school day as possible.

☐ Set goals for how much time to spend on each learning activity, such as reading silently for 20 minutes. Be sure to celebrate when goals are achieved.

☐ Plan ahead for when you need time for yourself. Explain when that will be, and help your child use a clock to know when that time is over.

☐ Include your child in planning out how to spend your time. Children are much more likely to stick with a plan when they had a part in deciding what it is.

Managing Space

☐ Identify one or more "learning spaces" around your home. Pick places that are as comfortable and distraction-free as possible.

☐ Use headphones to cancel out noise when it's not possible to create a distraction-free space.

☐ Collect containers such as shoeboxes or small cubbies to hold school items.

☐ Choose one area of the house to store school items when not in use. Having a dedicated place to "turn in" and "pick up" items helps keep things organized.

☐ Allow children to use outdoor spaces when possible. Outdoor spaces provide fresh air and can help lift moods. They can also provide fantastic learning opportunities themselves!

☐ Just like with the last note about time, include your child in planning out how to use your space, too.

—Team ABCmouse

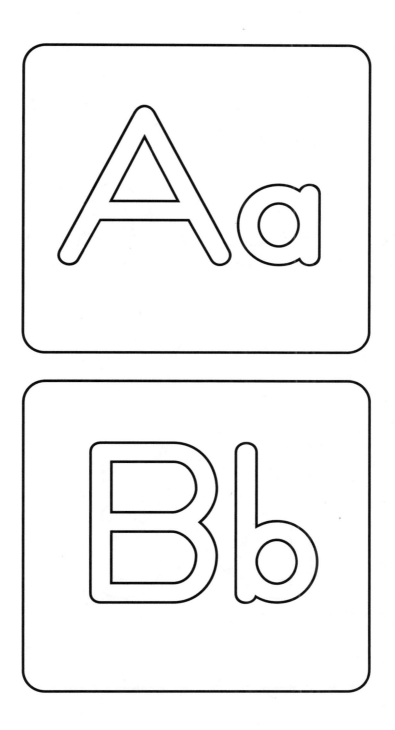

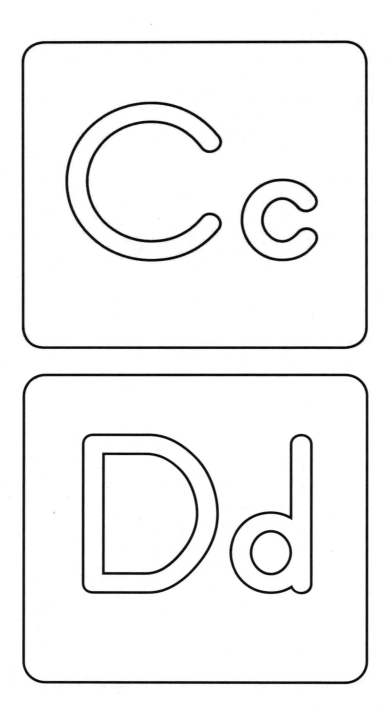

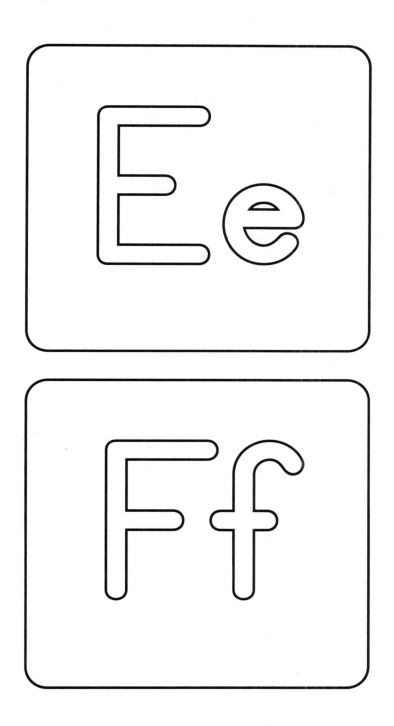

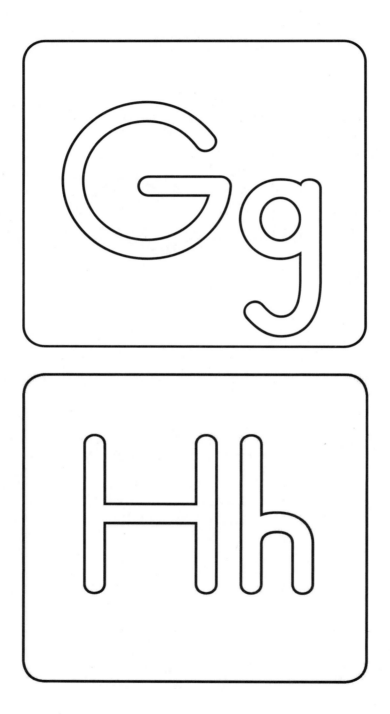

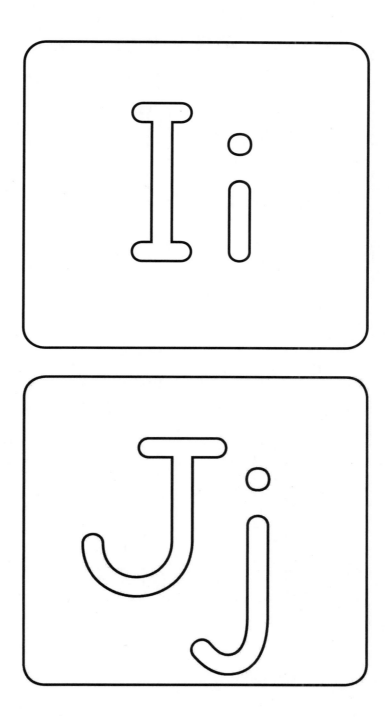

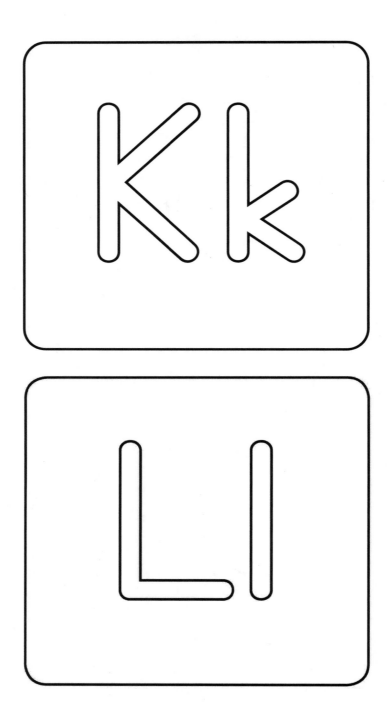

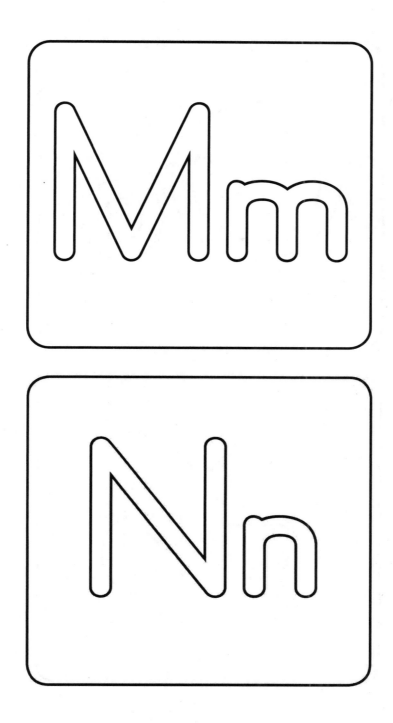

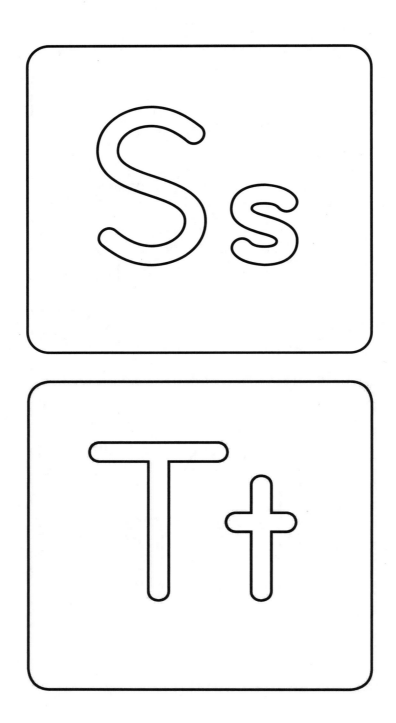

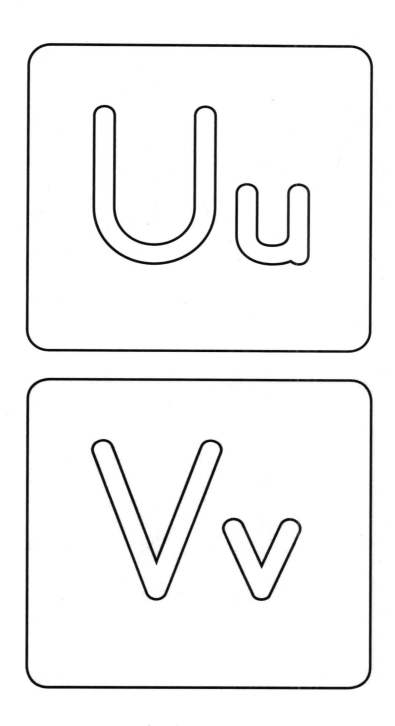

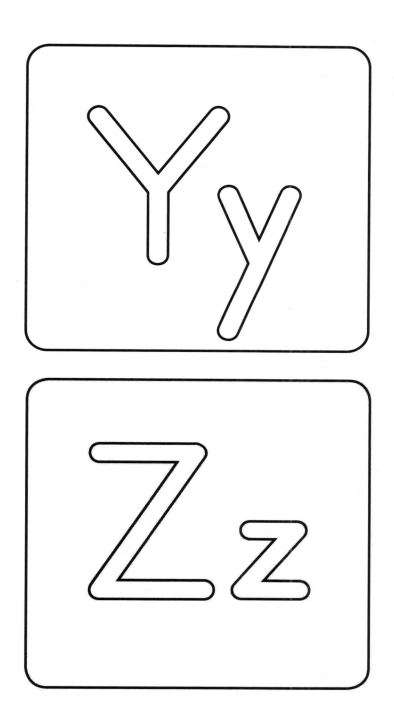

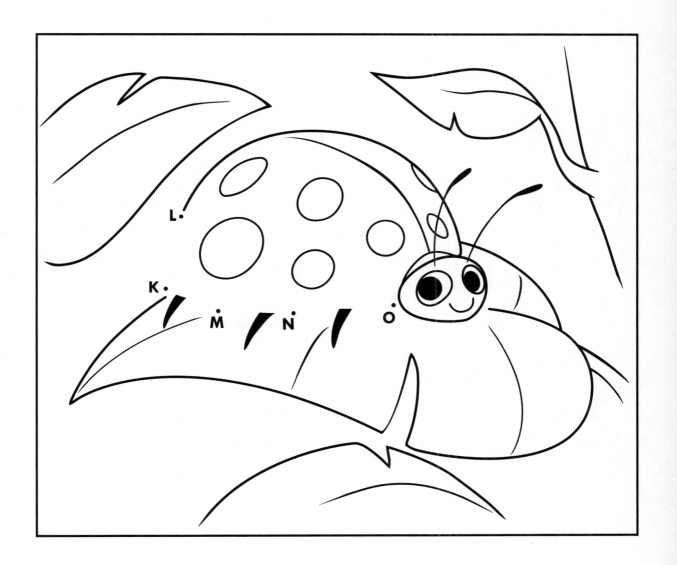

Match the letter to the picture.

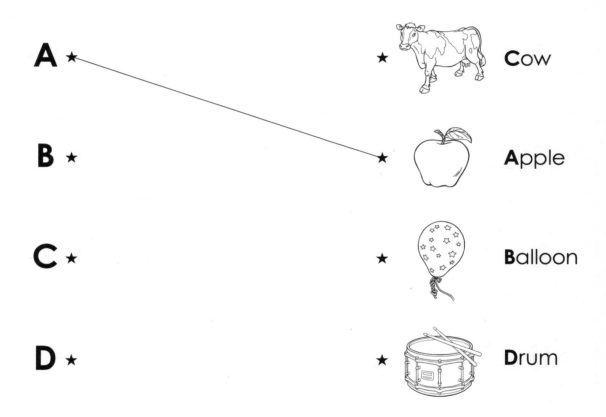

A ★   ★ **C**ow

B ★   ★ **A**pple

C ★   ★ **B**alloon

D ★   ★ **D**rum

Match the letter to the picture.

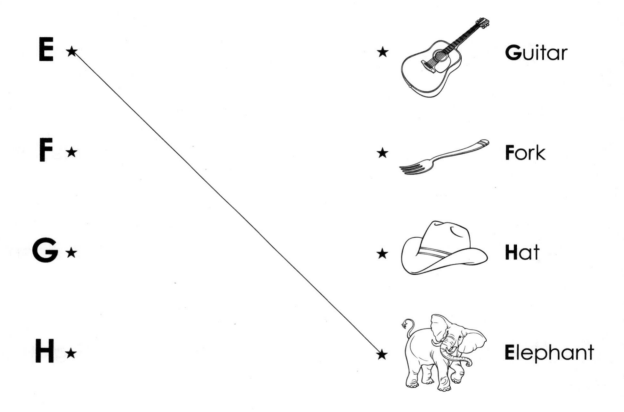

E ★

F ★

G ★

H ★

★ **G**uitar

★ **F**ork

★ **H**at

★ **E**lephant

Match the letter to the picture.

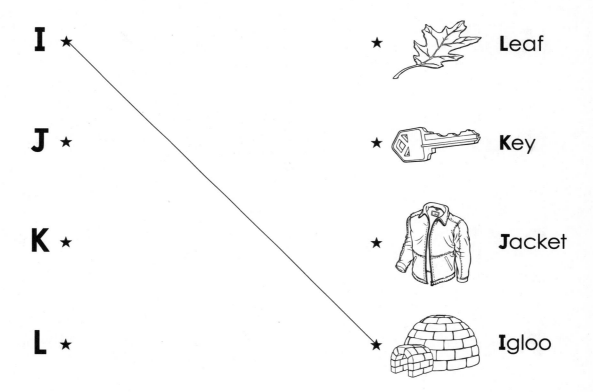

I ★

J ★

K ★

L ★

★ Leaf

★ Key

★ Jacket

★ Igloo

Match the letter to the picture.

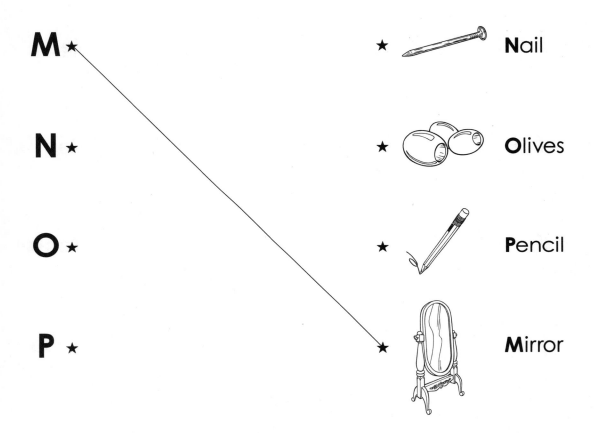

M ★

N ★

O ★

P ★

★ **N**ail

★ **O**lives

★ **P**encil

★ **M**irror

Match the letter to the picture.

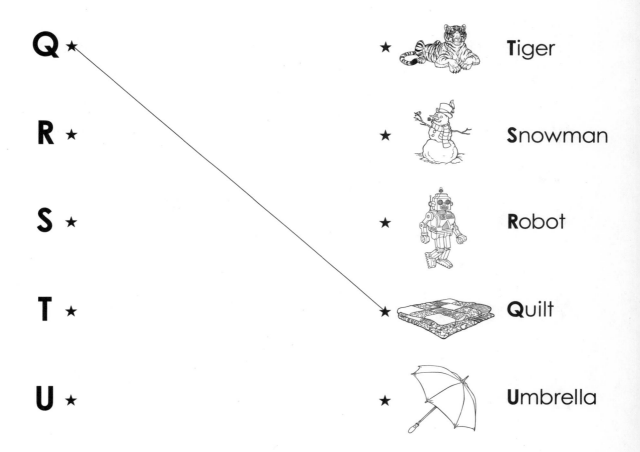

Q ★

R ★

S ★

T ★

U ★

★ **T**iger

★ **S**nowman

★ **R**obot

★ **Q**uilt

★ **U**mbrella

Match the letter to the picture.

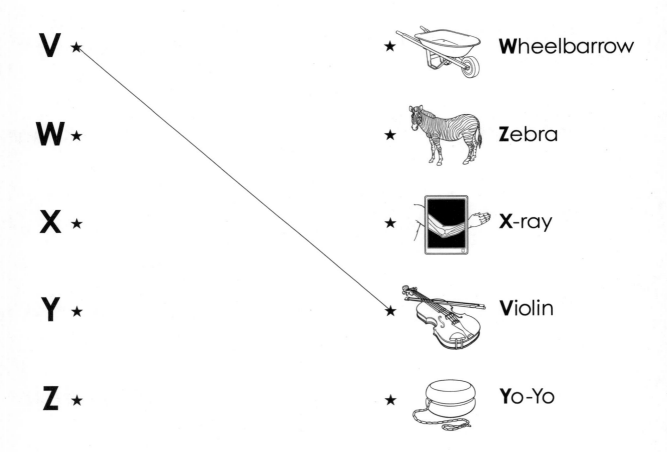

V ★

W ★

X ★

Y ★

Z ★

★ **W**heelbarrow

★ **Z**ebra

★ **X**-ray

★ **V**iolin

★ **Y**o-Yo

The Very Special Letter A

apple

acorn

A is for **a**pple.

a is for **a**corn

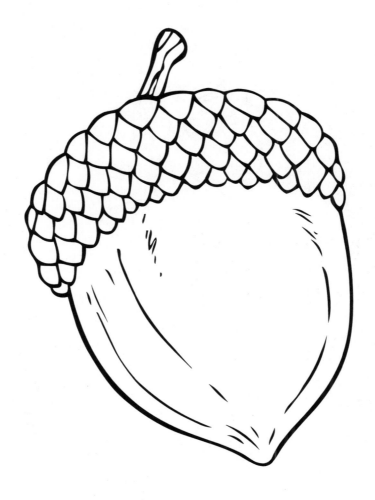

The Very Special Letter E

elephant

eagle

E is for elephant.

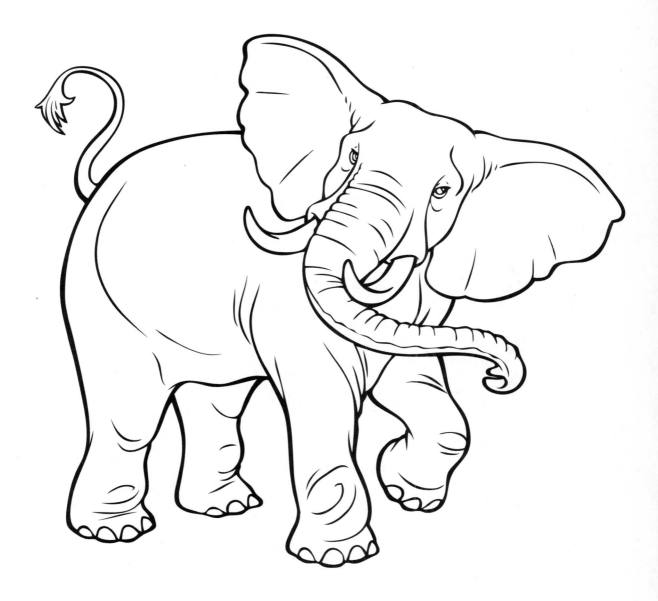

e is for **e**el

The Very Special Letter I

igloo

ice cream

I is for **i**gloo.

i is for **i**ce cube

The Very Special Letter O

olives

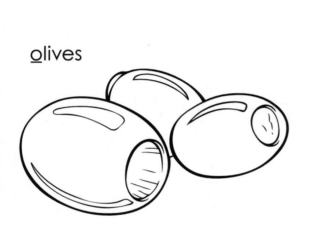

oval-shaped opal

O is for olives.

o is for **o**veralls

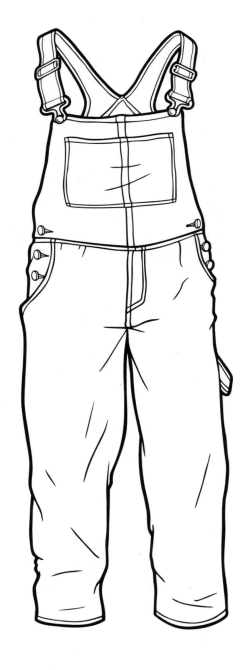

The Very Special Letter U

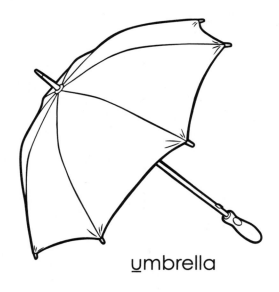

umbrella

unicorn

U is for **u**mbrella.

u is for unicycle

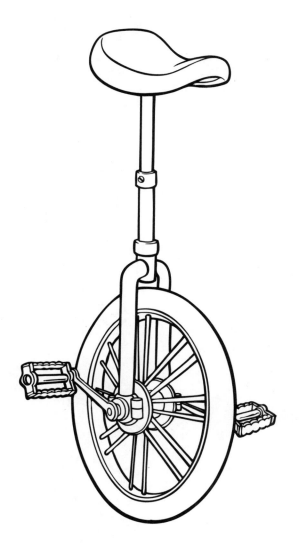

Look at each picture. Then choose a vowel (a, e, i, o, or u) to put in the middle so that the two words in the cross match the picture. Each vowel will be used only once. The first one has been done for you.

Color Key

ant: beige
ate: light blue
elf: white
eve: light green
itch: light brown
ivy: light gray
olive: green
old: dark green
up: peach
use: yellow

Find these things hidden in the picture.

apple ape   egg emu

igloo ice   ox oboe   umbrella ukulele

Find the items that go with these long vowel sound words in the picture.

skate   cake   bee   emu   bike

kite   rose   oboe   cube   ukelele

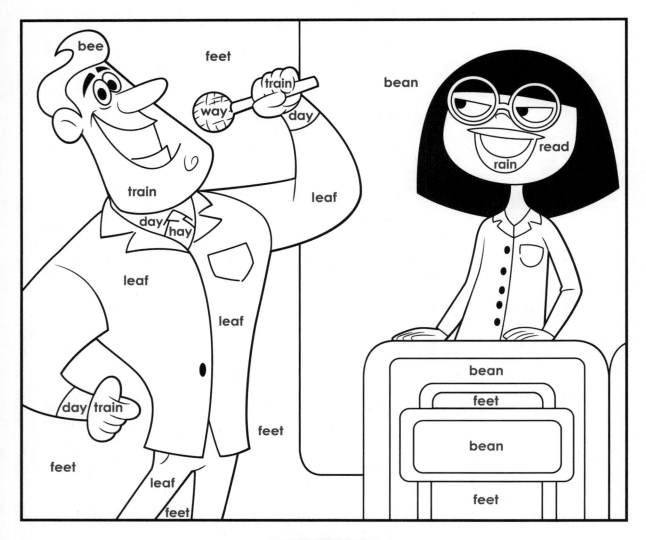

Color Key

train: peach
day: orange
bee: dark red
leaf: purple
hay: green
rain: red orange
read: tan
bean: light blue
feet: blue
way: gray

ABCmouse.com®
TM & © 2020 Age of Learning, Inc.

Find the items that go with these long vowel sound words in the picture.

fly   knight   pie

tie   arrow   boat   coat   crow

Look at the word bank.
Choose the correct word to write beneath each picture.

Word Bank

| man | cape | pine | cube | mane | cap | pin | cub |

_____   _____

_____   _____

_____   _____

_____   _____

Read the story. Circle the words with *oa* and *ow*.
Write each word under *oa* and *ow*.

Luis looks out the (window.)
He sees snow! Luis puts on
his coat. He runs outside.
The wind blows the snow
around. Soon Luis comes
back inside. Dad makes
him hot chocolate and
toast! *Yummy, yum, yum!*

oa

_____

_____

_____

ow

window

_____

_____

Read the sentence. Find a matching picture. Draw a line.

A.

1. The **statue** is very large.

2. Can you **rescue** my kitten?

B.

3. The **ewe** has a thick, woolly coat.

C.

4. My **nephew** likes to rollerblade.

D.

5. These **cashews** are yummy!

E.

Answer Key 1. D 2. A 3. E 4. C 5. B

Find these things hidden in the picture.

rake   cape   train

hay   cake   snake   grapes

Find these things hidden in the picture.

ice	bike	light
pie	kite	knight

Read a clue. Find the answer in the word box. Write the word in the puzzle.

Word Box

shorts	bark	horse	harp	dinner	farmer
car	horns	herd	yarn	porch	spider

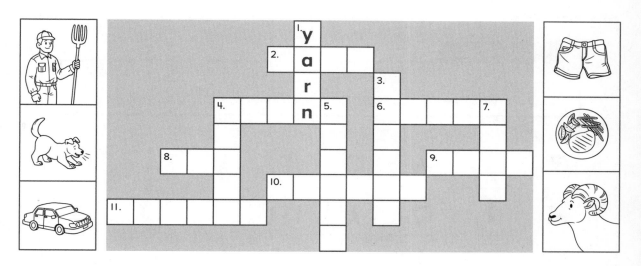

Across

2. This is a sound that a dog makes.

4. Some animals have these on their heads.

6. You can sit outside on this.

8. You wear a seat belt in this.

9. This is a group of animals.

10. This person grows vegetables.

11. This is what you eat at night.

Down

1. You can knit a blanket with this.

3. This insect spins webs.

4. This animal gallops.

5. You wear these when it's hot.

7. You play music with this.

Read a clue. Put the number of the clue next to the answer in the word box. Circle the word in the puzzle. The first one has been done for you.

Clues

1. Animals are raised on a ____ .
2. A ____ lives and works on a farm.
3. She ____ hard.
4. She plants ____ .

5. She feeds the ____ .
6. She gives ____ to the pigs to drink.
7. She puts hay in the ____ .
8. The farmer lives with ____ family.

Word Box

____ water	____ barn	____ her	____ farmer
____ works	I farm	____ corn	____ horses

```
e  j  w  o  r  y  l  c
k  f  a  r  m  i  g  o
u  x  t  k  d  h  e  r
p  b  e  x  v  o  r  n
f  a  r  m  e  r  p  d
y  r  v  i  t  s  z  b
g  n  q  u  h  e  c  r
l  w  o  r  k  s  a  n
```

Read a sentence. Circle the word with an ar, or, and er.
Draw a line from the sentence to the matching picture.

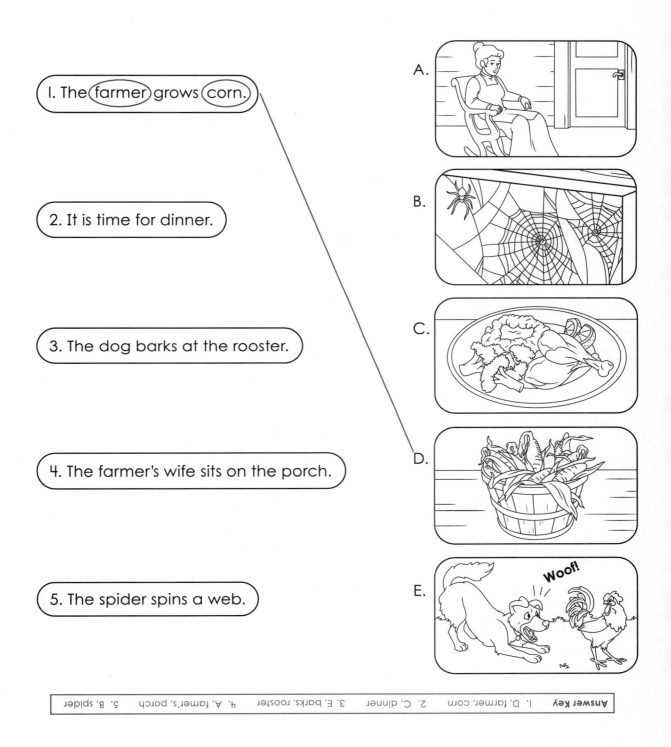

1. The (farmer) grows (corn.)

2. It is time for dinner.

3. The dog barks at the rooster.

4. The farmer's wife sits on the porch.

5. The spider spins a web.

A.

B.

C.

D.

E.

Woof!

Answer Key   1. D, farmer, corn   2. C, dinner   3. E, barks, rooster   4. A, famer's, porch   5. B, spider

Phonics Word Search
Spelling: long-vowel sounds

Read a clue. Put the number of the clue next to the answer in the word box. Circle the word in the puzzle. The first one has been done for you.

Clues

1. This is a piece of clothing. **c a pe**

2. This flies in the wind. **k___te**

3. You use this to get clean. **s ___ ___ p**

4. This word means very large. **h___ge**

5. This is what you do with a book. **r ___ ___ d**

6. This is drops of water falling from the sky. **r ___ ___ n**

7. This is something you can bake. **p___ ___**

8. This is a three-dimensional shape. **c ___ be**

9. This is something that grows on trees. **l ___ ___f**

10. This is found on your face. **n ___ se**

Word Box

rain	nose	cape	huge	kite	leaf	read	cube	pie	soap

```
h  c  p  i  v  m  g  r
r  a  i  n  t  s  b  l
e  j  e  y  n  o  s  e
a  w  l  e  q  a  o  a
d  o  k (c  a  p  e) f
t  r  h  u  g  e  v  i
c  z  u  b  x  j  m  d
k  i  t  e  f  w  y  n
```

Find the items that go with these long vowel sound words in the picture.

train   hay   light   tie

coat   crow   leaf   bee   fly

Look at the picture. Read the sentence. Write the missing word.
Hint: every missing word has a long vowel sound.

1. Do you think that a _____ can float?

2. May I have more _____ , please?

3. Which is the best _____? It's a tie!

4. It's easy to see a _____ in the snow.

5. I fall asleep better with a bright

   night- _____ .

Language Arts Word Search

Words with *er*, *ur*, and *ir*

Read a clue. Put the number of the clue next to the answer in the word box.
Circle the word in the puzzle. The first one has been done for you.

Word Box

1 tower	____ dirt	____ thirsty
____ purple	____ surf	____ over
____ curly	____ hammer	____ bird

```
k   d   s   c   l   g   w   o   q
t   s   w   b   i   r   d   v   p
h   z   h   k   t   o   w   e   r
i   v   a   m   m   i   c   r   w
r   s   m   i   r   e   d   k   e
s   u   m   s   r   g   i   y   g
t   r   e   c   c   u   r   l   y
y   f   r   o   e   p   t   m   s
p   u   r   p   l   e   a   w   j
```

Clues

1. That _____ is 20 stories tall.
2. The _____ perched on a branch.
3. The _____ cat drank water from its bowl.
4. I walked _____ the bridge.
5. The gardener planted seeds in the _____.
6. Plums and eggplants are both _____.
7. The poodle has _____ fur.
8. When you _____, you ride on waves in the ocean.
9. The builder hit the nail with his _____.

Answer Key I. tower; 2. bird; 3. thirsty; 4. over; 5. dirt; 6. purple; 7. curly; 8. surf; 9. hammer

Read a clue. Put the number of the clue next to the answer in the word box.
Circle the word in the puzzle.

Clues

1. There are five of these on a foot.

2. Farm animals eat this.

3. This is water that falls from the sky.

4. You wear this when it is cold.

5. You put soup in this.

6. A horse makes this sound.

7. This is a kind of meat.

Word Box

_____ rain   _____ steak

_____ hay   _____ coat

_____ neigh   _____ bowl

_____ toes

```
u  b  s  t  e  d  p  k  a
l  x  t  v  i  l  c  b  f
k  n  e  i  g  h  z  o  m
y  r  a  f  h  q  u  w  o
e  m  k  x  b  o  n  l  g
c  o  a  t  a  f  r  u  e
o  q  p  o  i  h  a  y  v
s  g  w  e  z  m  i  d  t
v  u  d  s  r  e  n  p  y
```

Look at the poem and the picture. Write the missing letters in the poem.
Use the word part box to help you. Then color the picture.

ey	ea	ie	igh	ea	ee	ay	ea	ai	oa

Owen's Odd Appetite

Owen liked to ____t strange things:

Like turk____ on corn flakes.

Or ____tmeal, p____ches, and dr____d fish

All blended into shakes.

So on his birthd____ n____t, he didn't

Want to have pl____n cake.

Instead he had gr____n frosting spread

On medium-rare st____k!

Look at the pictures and the words. Some of the letters are missing!
Choose the right vowel team from the three next to the word.
Then write those letters in the blanks to complete the word.

	ay / oa / oi	h_____
	oa / ai / igh	d_____sy
	ee / igh / oi	sh____p
	ay / ea / ie	b____n
	ie / ow / ai	r____sins

Look at each picture. Find a word in the box. Write the word.

Word Box

boat rain pie peas crow hay statue knight feet cashews

①  crow

②

③

④

⑤

⑥

⑦

⑧

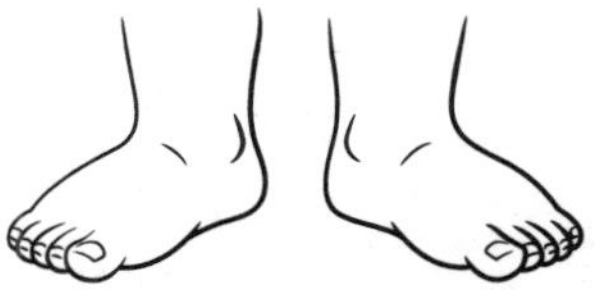

⑨

⑩

Look at the picture and read the word for it. Circle the word that has the same vowel sounds. Write that word in the blank.

Picture	Words	Write
train	bean (play)	play
feet	team / paint	
pie	dream / night	
tray	rain / tree	
cheese	tie / meat	

Word Writing

Words with igh, oa, ow, ew, and ue

Look at the picture. Read the word next to it.
Find a word in the box with the same long vowel sound. Write the word.

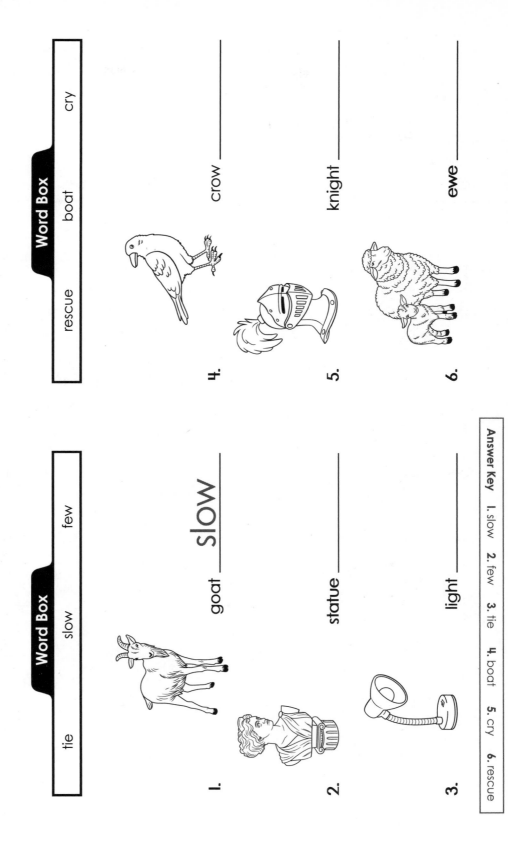

Word Box

tie	slow	few

1. goat _slow_

2. statue _____

3. light _____

Word Box

rescue	boat	cry

4. crow _____

5. knight _____

6. ewe _____

Crossword
Vowel Teams

Write the missing letters to make the words in the word box.

Look at each picture. Find a word in the box. Write the word.

Word Box

| tray | seeds | chain | beads | knight | pie | ewe | coat | statue | crow |

1. chain

2. _____

3. _____

4. _____

5. _____

6. _____

7. _____

8. _____

9. _____

10. _____

Look at the picture and say the word. Circle the two letters that stand for the vowel sound. Copy the letters. Trace the rest of the letters to write the word.

	au	all	s t r
	al	aw	
	au	all	f c e t
	al	aw	
	au	all	c h k
	al	aw	
	au	all	w k
	al	aw	
	au	all	h k
	al	aw	

Read a clue. Put the number of the clue next to the answer in the word box. Circle the word in the puzzle. The first one has been done for you.

Clues

1. A _____ is connected to a leg.
2. You see the ____ in the sky.
3. A chair can be made out of ____.
4. You sweep the floor with a ____.

5. You can swim in a ____.
6. I like to read a good ____.
7. You go to a ____ to learn.
8. I wear a ____ when it rains.

Word Box

| ____ moon | 1 foot | ____ hood | ____ pool |
| ____ book | ____ school | ____ wood | ____ broom |

```
n  g  a  z  b  o  o  k
m  w  o  o  r  e  y  u
p  x  t  j  o  h  z  c
o  s  c  h  o  o  l  e
o  k  i  f  m  o  o  n
l  u  w  o  o  d  s  g
d  h  o  o  v  b  i  p
a  r  v  t  j  q  f  y
```

Look at the picture. Read the word for it. Draw a line to a word that has the same long vowel sound. You can color the pictures.

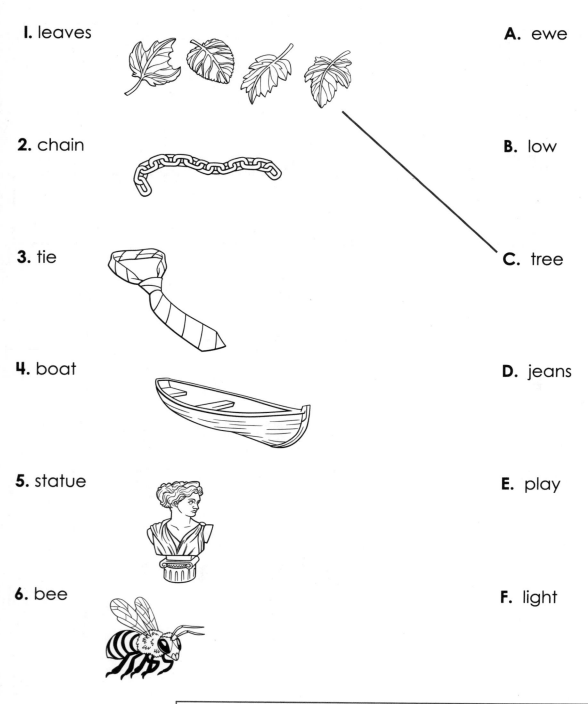

I. leaves

A. ewe

2. chain

B. low

3. tie

C. tree

4. boat

D. jeans

5. statue

E. play

6. bee

F. light

Answer Key **I.** C (or D) **2.** E **3.** F **4.** B **5.** A **6.** D (or C)

Have an adult cut out the cards. Read each word.
Sort the cards into three piles: words with *ie*, *igh*, and *y*.
Put each set of cards together to make a picture

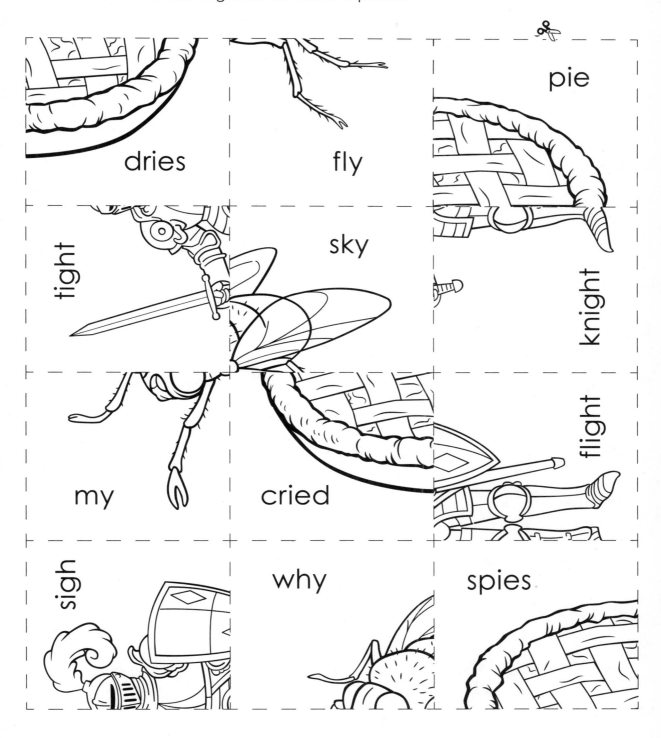

dries

fly

pie

tight

sky

knight

my

cried

flight

sigh

why

spies

Cut and fold to create a book!

— — — cut line ———— fold line

4

He sees a chest floating in the sea.

3

Lee unties his boat from the dock.

5

Lee can't wait to see what the chest contains.

2

Read the story. Underline each long vowel team you see.

The Fun Feast at Sea

6

The chest is loaded with peaches!

7

Lee and his seagull have a fun feast.

Word Bank

Lee	unties
boat	sees
floating	sea
wait	see
contains	loaded
peaches	seagull
great	feast

ABCmouse.com®